You and your sight

living with a sight problem

by

Hilary Todd and Francesca Wolf

**with an introduction by
Claire Rayner**

London : HMSO

First published 1994

ISBN 0 11 701797 3

This book is also available on audio tape and in braille.
Enquiries about these editions should be sent direct to
RNIB Customer Services, PO Box 173, Peterborough
PE2 6WS, telephone 0345-023153 (for the price of a
local call).

In loving memory of
David Scott

Contents

Introduction

Some thirty or so years ago at a family wedding I was sitting with a group of elderly great aunts who were bemoaning the fate of a distant cousin who, at 30, was suffering severe sight loss. One of the aunts asked me what advice anyone could possibly offer to someone with such a 'terrible progressive disease'. I said, 'Learn braille, so that when you're blind, you'll find it easier to cope.'

The aunts were scandalised and scolded me roundly for even saying the word 'blind' and for being so 'pessimistic'. But I stood my ground and assured them I thought that was the most optimistic way to go - to acknowledge the reality of the problem and prepare accordingly.

They are long since gone, those angry aunts, but I wish they were here now to see this book - because it bears out exactly what I was trying to explain to them all that time ago. That there is life after loss of sight, and that intelligent planning, logical organising and positive thinking can make life more than merely tolerable, but as enriching as it is for anyone else.

To make that possible, however, you need information. Information is the key that opens the door to everything, and this book is therefore to be seen as a large and very easy to use key.

The information it offers is fascinating as well as useful. Understanding what happens to sight, what can be done to deal with loss of vision, what the aids and treatments are, is obviously of prime importance.

But so are the nitty gritty details of day-to-day living, ranging from coping with ordinary letters to cooking and cleaning, shopping and travelling. Sorting out money matters is considered in admirably accessible terms and so is the matter of earning a living - the jobs and training section makes particularly good reading.

And there's information too, for the families and friends of people who are having sight problems, as well as news for parents of children who can't see properly, covering such issues as education and holidays.

It's all here, in other words. Maybe you'll read it in print, or maybe in braille, or listen on tape. Whatever method you use to get this information, you'll find it of huge value. As one who has needed glasses for years and is well aware of the fact that they seem to have to be stronger at each checkup and also as a writer whose readers have for years reached me via braille, Moon and audio tape, I found material here I was grateful to know. It comforted me.

In a way I learned braille when I read this book. Not literally - but in an emotional sense. Getting ready for reality is what this book is about - and whether severe sight loss arrives or not, it doesn't matter - I'll be ready for it.

Claire Rayner

Acknowledgments

Many people contributed to the making of this book. We owe particular thanks to our expert colleagues in RNIB: Chris Attrill, Marcus Weisen and Alan Wetherly of Leisure Services; Andy Barrick, Laura Jacobs and Moira Routledge of the Benefit Rights and Information Team; Nancy Chambers of the Education Information Service; Mark Davies, Development Officer for Older People; Bernard Fleming of the Community Education Office; Sue Grindey, Sheena McBride and Veronica Bevan of the Health Services Development Unit; Jan Nesbitt of the Personnel Department; Kishor Patel, Development Officer for Ethnic Minorities; Jeremy Porteus of the Housing Service; Sean Thompson of Employment Network; and Margaret Wilson-Hinds of Customer Services. Many other RNIB colleagues have made helpful comments on various drafts.

Especial thanks go to everyone in RNIB's Publications Unit: to Sharon Stokes for word-processing innumerable drafts; Deborah Wickham for her graphic design skills; Gill Pawley for proof-reading; Natasha Dhalla for arranging the taping and brailling; and Rachel Hone and Judith Riley for their professional support. Thanks also go to our colleagues in the Talking Book Studios and Braille Services for their support.

In addition to colleagues, several people gave advice on the final draft from the readers' point of view. We would like to thank Ken Bodden, Sandra Horsfall, the late Leslie Smith and Mary Smith, Edna Scott and Rachel Wolf.

A number of photographers have allowed us to use their work in this book. Our thanks go to Max Hampson, Richard Hancock, Crispin Hughes, Sally Lancaster, Isabel Lilly, Michael Hannaford, Unit 18 Photography, Norwich and Neil Walker.

Finally, we would like to record our gratitude to Claire Rayner and to our publishers, HMSO, in particular to Judith Tassell and Valerie Taylor, whose professionalism and enthusiasm for this book never faltered.

Hilary Todd
Francesca Wolf

About the authors

Hilary Todd is Information Services Manager at RNIB, with responsibility for the Publications Unit and other information and training services in RNIB's External Relations Division. A writer and editor for many years, she has also worked in the fields of ageing, social policy and education.

Francesca Wolf is a freelance editor and writer, specialising in health, education and family matters. She contributes to a wide range of publications including *The Times Educational Supplement, Parents* and *Here's Health* and has written and produced publications for many charities.

How to use this book

This book is arranged in eight chapters covering major topic areas. It also has an introductory list of agencies that can help, two address lists and a short guide to benefits. Few people will want or need to read it from cover to cover, so we suggest you start with the contents list on pages v to ix to pick out a general subject that interests you. However, we hope everyone will find helpful Chapter 1 (Understanding your sight problem) and Chapter 5 (Money matters) .

There is an index (pages 137-148) for readers who wish to check on a particular subject which may or may not appear in the contents list. If, for example, you want to read about the new 'Access to Work' scheme, you will find it in the index.

Further reading is listed at the ends of most chapters. In many cases we have given a supplier for the suggested reading, but you can, of course, use your public library and local bookseller to obtain most books. Leaflets and factsheets usually have to be obtained direct from the publisher. If you need further advice on books to read, please contact RNIB's Reference Library (address 36 on page 126) .

A beginner's guide to the main organisations which can help

This book refers to various organisations which can help you. In case you're not familiar with them, or don't know where to find them in your area, we've provided this explanatory list of the main ones. Others are listed on pages 119 to 130.

Benefits Agency - this is the government department which deal with pensions, income support and other such benefits. Local offices used to be known as 'social security offices'. There are offices throughout the country, whose telephone numbers you can find through Directory Enquiries. (There is a free Directory Enquiry Service for people who cannot read telephone books - see page 32 for details.) Your local public library will help you with addresses.

Citizens Advice Bureaux - these provide free advice on a wide range of topics. There is a branch in most towns. You can find the address from your public library.

Jobcentres - these are run by the Department of Employment to help you find or keep a job. Jobcentres are usually found on the high street, or ask Directory Enquiries for the telephone number.

Social Services Department - this department of your local council provides community care services like home helps, social work and (sometimes) a specialised service for people with visual impairments. Contact your local town hall to find the address of the office nearest to you or telephone Directory Enquiries.

In Scotland, this department is known as the **Social Work Department**, and in Northern Ireland as **Health and Social Services Boards**.

Royal National Institute for the Blind (RNIB) - is the leading organisation for people with serious sight problems. RNIB provides more than 60 different services throughout the UK. Many though not all of our services are mentioned in this book. Please contact us for further advice if you want information or help. Addresses and telephone numbers are given on pages 126-129.

Voluntary association/society for the blind - these local groups provide a range of services such as clubs, home visitors and sometimes rehabilitation. They work with people with all degrees of sight loss. Most areas of the country have a voluntary society, though they vary widely in their activities. Contact your local public library to find out the address of your nearest society, or telephone RNIB's Voluntary Agencies Link Unit (address 36 on page 126) which has a list of all of them.

1 Understanding your sight problem

1.1 Does our eyesight get worse with age?

Ageing affects the whole of our bodies and our eyes are no exception. Most people will notice small changes in their sight from the middle years onwards. Typically, people find it increasingly difficult to read small print or thread a fine needle. These changes are perfectly normal and can usually be corrected by spectacles.

But it's very important to distinguish between these normal changes in your sight and eye disease. Although we are all more likely to get an eye disease as we get older, we should never

accept worsening sight as an unavoidable aspect of ageing. If you notice any unusual changes in your sight - perhaps distortion, or spots in front of your eyes, or everything appearing dim -

then it's important to get medical advice **straight away**. If you are found to have an eye disease, then the sooner treatment is started, the better. Never put your sight problem down to 'old age' and ignore it.

1.2 Should I go to my doctor or would it be best to see an optician?

We suggest that you see your own doctor first. He or she may send you to an optician (optometrist) with a note, or may refer you straight to a hospital eye department. But it doesn't really matter whom you see so long as you do it promptly.

If your sight changes very suddenly - and, of course, if you have an accident involving your eyes - then you should go straight to the nearest hospital with a casualty department or eye clinic. If you have diabetes you should be particularly careful about sight changes and get to your doctor or a hospital quickly if you notice anything unusual.

If your doctor suspects an eye disease, you may be referred to various specialists. It is helpful to know who does what:

- An **optometrist** (previously called an **optician** and sometimes an **ophthalmic optician**) works in a high street practice or a hospital. Optometrists are qualified to test sight and prescribe glasses, to detect eye conditions and refer you if necessary to a GP or ophthalmologist. They are not qualified to treat or operate on your eyes although they will often discuss your eye condition with you.

- A 'dispensing optician', now known simply as an **optician**, is qualified to supply and fit glasses, not to prescribe them or test sight.

- An **orthoptist** treats certain eye disorders such as squints and lazy eyes. Orthoptists always work in hospitals under the direction of an ophthalmologist.

- An **ophthalmologist** is a doctor who specialises in eyes. Most of these specialists work in hospital eye clinics and they are qualified to diagnose eye conditions, treat them and perform surgery if necessary.

1.3 How do our eyes work? What can go wrong?

In order to be able to see, three bits of apparatus need to work properly - the eye, the optic nerve, and the brain.

The **eye** is a complex and delicate structure. Its job is to focus rays of light onto the retina, at the back of the eye, where special cells convert the light rays into electrical impulses. These electrical impulses are sent to the brain by the **optic nerve** and, finally, the **brain** decodes the information to enable us to see. The diagram below shows an eye in cross section. Something can go wrong with any of the parts of the eye

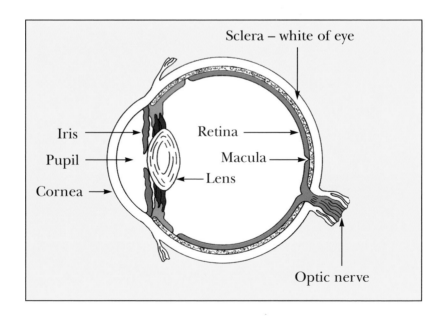

or with the optic nerve or the brain. In the UK, the four commonest eye conditions are:

● **Cataract** is a condition which affects the lens, making it cloudy instead of clear. If you have a cataract your vision tends to be misty and indistinct, especially in strong sunshine. Cataracts can usually be successfully treated by removing the lens and either inserting an artificial one or prescribing special glasses.

Cataract can make your vision misty and blurred

● **Macular degeneration** affects a small area of special cells on the back of the retina called the macula. Normally this little area of cells enables us to see fine detail, such as print. If the macula becomes diseased, however, much of your central vision is lost so that reading, sewing and even recognising faces becomes very difficult. But side vision remains so that you can usually move around safely and carry on with many normal activities. Macular degeneration is largely found in older people and though it cannot be cured, treatment in the very early stages can help.

Macular degeneration affects central vision, though side vision remains

- **Glaucoma** is usually caused by raised pressure in the eye. This has nothing to do with blood pressure, but with the pressure of the watery fluid inside your eye. If this fluid does not drain away at the same rate it is produced, then the pressure inside the eye rises. If untreated this pressure can damage the retina, reducing your side vision. Glaucoma can be treated successfully by eye drops or tablets, but only if treatment is started early.

Glaucoma tends to run in families, so it's important to have your eyes tested regularly if you have a close relative with glaucoma

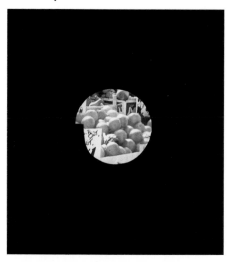

(eye tests are free for people over 40 who are at risk this way). People of Afro-Caribbean origin are also a high-risk group - and at a younger age (from the late 20s).

Advanced glaucoma can result in tunnel vision

- **Diabetic retinopathy** is an eye condition that affects some people with diabetes. The condition leads to bleeding from the retina, the spots of blood in the eye causing patchy or blurred vision. Sometimes this bleeding into the eye clears up by itself, but early treatment can also stop the bleeding in many cases and prevent serious sight loss. This is why it is very important for people with diabetes to look after their sight - to have an annual sight check and seek medical help quickly if anything goes wrong.

Diabetic retinopathy can produce patchy and blurred vision

There are many other diseases which can affect the eyes. Other conditions can affect the optic nerve (which can sometimes also be damaged by head injury) or the brain itself. Some people who have had a stroke lose some of their sight for instance.

Sight problems are common. In the UK almost a million people have sight problems serious enough for them to be counted as 'blind' or 'partially sighted' for registration purposes (registration is explained on page 26). Another 700,000 people have sight problems which make it difficult to read ordinary newspaper print. By the time we are 75 or over as many as one in seven of us will have an eye condition. It's also possible to have more than one eye condition which is why, even if you already have one eye defect, you must still have your sight tested regularly.

But although sight problems are common, total blindness is quite rare. Many people fear that, if they've got an eye condition, they will eventually go completely blind. This rarely happens, for most people retain some useful sight, even when their eye condition is quite advanced. The pictures above show what people with each of the four common eye diseases may be able to see. Ask your ophthalmologist to explain what is likely to happen in your case.

1.4 Where can I get more information about my eye condition?

Many national and local groups have been set up to provide information about eye conditions. We have listed the main national ones on pages 119–121. Do get in touch with these groups. Many offer not just information but also support, advice and encouragement from people who know the problems.

At local level, most cities, towns and counties have a 'society for the blind'. Don't be put off by the name, for these societies will help anyone with a serious sight problem. Local societies may be able to provide information about your eye condition and much more besides. You can find out about your local society from your public library, the Citizens Advice Bureau, your social worker or from RNIB's Voluntary Agencies Link Unit (address 36 on page 126) which keeps a list of all of them.

You will also find information about eye conditions in the publications listed at the end of this chapter.

1.5 Can eye conditions be prevented or slowed down?

As mentioned in question 1.3 above, many eye conditions can be helped by early treatment (for example, glaucoma and diabetic retinopathy). Whether these and other eye conditions can be prevented in the first place is debatable, because most eye diseases are not fully understood.

Scientists are now beginning to study the effects of vitamins and minerals on vision. Early findings suggest that healthy eyes have much to do with a healthy, well balanced diet. In other words, look after your general health and you'll also be looking after your eyes. This is especially important in older age when we're all more at risk of eye problems.

Some people claim to have been helped by holistic or complementary medicine (such as homoeopathy, acupuncture, naturopathy). There is little scientific evidence about the effectiveness of these therapies either in preventing or treating eye conditions. If you have an interest in these alternatives, do discuss it with your doctor first. Never stop taking any prescribed drops or tablets for an eye condition without checking with your doctor that it is safe to do so.

Please make sure you're never the victim of an eye injury. Every day over 200 people need hospital treatment for an eye injury that happens at home. Most of these injuries are preventable. Buy a pair of safety goggles and wear them when

A pair of safety goggles, costing as little as £3, can prevent serious eye injuries. You should always wear them when drilling and other DIY and gardening jobs

you do DIY jobs (drilling, paint stripping, sanding and tile-cutting are especially risky), work underneath your car, prune the roses or use a strimmer in the garden. Put corks on the tops of your garden canes. Use oven cleaner, bleach, glue and fireworks very carefully. This advice applies to all of us but especially to people who already have an eye condition.

1.6 I need to go into hospital for an eye operation. What will this involve?

It's natural to feel anxious if you need to go into hospital for any operation, perhaps more so in the case of eye surgery.

It usually helps to discuss your operation in detail with your specialist or an ophthalmic nurse. Nowadays, most eye patients spend only a short time in hospital. Some cataract operations, for example, are done in day clinics - so you can go home on the day of your operation. For other operations you may need to spend a few days in hospital.

Some people assume that eye surgery involves laser treatment. This is not necessarily the case. For example, cataracts are removed by surgery but if adjustments are needed later, these might be done by laser. Again, your specialist will tell you what is planned in your case. Whatever surgical technique is being used, do ask your specialist (or a nurse) what degree of discomfort to expect, what you will be able to see when you 'come round', and what to expect in the days and weeks after the operation. The more you know in advance, the easier it will be to face it.

If a hospital stay is troubling you because you have a dependent relative or a pet, ask to see the hospital social worker. She can help to make arrangements for dependants while you are in hospital and during your convalescence.

1.7 What are 'low vision aids' and where do I get them from?

'Low vision aids' are devices which help you to see better. The simplest is an ordinary magnifier and perhaps the most complex is a closed-circuit television which enlarges print to your chosen size. There are also magnifiers with a built-in light, small telescopes for viewing distant objects such as bus numbers, and special lenses which can be mounted on your spectacles.

Low vision aids can help many (though not all) people who have some residual sight. Choosing the right one is important and you will need professional help. Ask your ophthalmologist for a referral to a low vision service. She may refer you to a 'low vision clinic' in a hospital or to an optometrist specialising in this work. One of the advantages of the hospital low vision service is that you can usually borrow aids from them. These clinics and specialists are not found everywhere, unfortunately, but if you have

difficulty, contact the Partially Sighted Society for advice (address 34 on page 126). Many local societies for 'the blind' can also help with advice.

A special lens mounted on spectacles helps this lady to read large-print books

1.8 Is it ever possible to come to terms with sight loss?

The simple answer is 'yes', but this can be slow, painful and difficult. Sight is the most crucial of our five senses and to lose it (or most of it) can be a traumatic experience. But everyone is different, so reactions to sight loss vary a great deal.

Many people liken sight loss to a bereavement, and in some ways it is. It is quite natural for you to feel shock and disbelief at first, then anger, grief and depression as the truth about your loss begins to sink in. And just as with the newly bereaved, people around you, though usually well-meaning, can be insensitive. Some will try to cheer you up by telling you about the heroic things blind people can do these days - when you feel barely human, let alone superhuman.

Others will try to over-protect you by preventing you from tackling a task you're perfectly capable of doing. Some can even come out with some very hurtful remarks, such as, 'she can see well enough when she wants to'. Many will simply be embarrassed by your disability and either shun you completely or never mention it. All of this can add to your own difficulties and make you feel even more depressed, frustrated and angry.

There are two things you have to face that you may find very painful. The first is that you will need help to do some things you once took for granted. You may need help to read your post, or cross a road or do the shopping. It can be very hard to lose your independence this way and have to rely on others.

The second difficulty is having to accept a new 'label' and all that goes with it. Society is still remarkably insensitive to people with disabilities. You may have to get used to being called 'the blind woman/man' as though your sight problem somehow says it all. You may hear people make excuses for you as though you were unable to hear, walk and think. It can be just as maddening to hear people call you 'wonderful' because you're able to do things for yourself! Another aspect of this labelling is having to use some painful words to describe yourself, for instance if you're claiming benefits or asking for help from your town hall. The words 'disabled', 'visually impaired' or 'partially sighted' tend to stick in the throat.

Coming to terms with sight loss has been described as a journey and, as with many journeys, it helps to find a companion, or better still a guide.

Talking to someone about your feelings and what you are going through can be a great help. Ask your eye specialist or the social services department if they have a counselling service or rehabilitation workers. Counselling services are rare, but if people do not ask for this service, it never will be provided. Your doctor might know of local counselling services, though it's unusual to find general counsellors who know anything about sight loss. You can also contact the British Association for Counselling for information (address 8 on page 122).

The best guides are people who have made the journey before you. That's why it's useful to join an association for people with your eye condition, or to get in touch with your local society for 'the blind' (meaning anyone with serious sight problems). Some of the main associations are listed on page 119; you can get details of your local society from public libraries, or your social worker, or from RNIB's Voluntary Agencies Link Unit which keeps a list of all of them (address 36 on page 126). There are also some useful books you can read and we've listed a few below. Talking to someone else who shares your eye problem can be a real help.

Eventually most people find they can accept their sight loss and realise that, although they may need help to do some things, they can get on with their lives all the same. Sight loss is not the end, but the start of a new, different and challenging chapter in your life. The rest of this book describes some of the commonest challenges you are likely to face and offers practical advice to help you meet them.

Further reading

BBC In Touch publications

Coping again: better sight for elderly people with central vision loss. An In Touch Care Guide, 1993
(£3.50. In large print, braille or on tape)

The In Touch Handbook, edited by Margaret Ford and Thena Heshel, annual. (£17.95. Available in large print, braille or on tape)

Waiting to see? Information for people with cataracts. An In Touch Care Guide, 1993
(£2.50. In large print, braille or on tape)

In Touch publications are available from Broadcasting Support Services, PO Box 7, London W3 6XJ.

RNIB leaflets

All about cataracts
All about diabetic retinopathy
All about glaucoma
All about age-related macular degeneration
(Available in print, braille or on tape from RNIB Customer Services, address 38 on page 127)

Other publications

Eyes - their problems and treatment, by Michael Glasspool. Martin Dunitz, 1984 (Out of print, but possibly available through your public library. A copy is held in RNIB Reference Library, address 36 on page 126. Available in print)

Touching the rock: an experience of blindness, by John M Hull. SPCK, 1990 (£4.99. Also available in braille (National Library for the Blind), as a talking book (RNIB Talking Book Service) and on tape (Calibre) - addresses 31, 45 and 12 on pages 125, 129 and 123)

NB It is always worth asking at your hospital whether they have any leaflets about your eye condition.

2 Registering your sight problem

2.1 What is registration? How do I get on the register?

All social services departments (social work departments in Scotland, Health and Social Services Boards in Northern Ireland) keep registers of people with serious sight problems. The aim is to ensure as far as possible that people with disabling loss of sight are offered help. Many (though not all) social services departments employ a specialist social worker who will visit people on the register and assess their needs for information and practical help. If you are not registered you are less likely to receive this help. The registers are held in complete confidence - names are not even passed on to charities like RNIB or local societies for 'the blind' (unless there is an 'agency' agreement).

If you wish to register, discuss it with your hospital eye specialist (ophthalmologist) or ask your doctor to refer you to a specialist. He will assess your visual loss and will recommend your registration as either 'blind' or 'partially sighted'. (It is not easy to explain these words precisely, in lay terms, for there are 'blind' people who have some vision, and the distinction between blindness and partial sight is never simple.) Once the ophthalmologist has assessed your sight, he will complete a form (form BD8 in England and Wales, BP1 in Scotland and A655 in Northern Ireland). You get one copy of the form and another is sent to the social services department, who should then send a social worker to visit you. When the social worker visits you he will ask if you wish to be added to the register.

2.2   What are the advantages in registering?

Registration has a number of advantages. It is a key into the system which qualifies you for some financial benefits and special concessions including:

- extra income tax relief if you are a tax payer

- slightly more generous treatment for under-80s who are entitled to income support, housing benefit or council tax benefit

- some travel, car parking and other concessions

- eligibility for severe disablement allowance (see page 67) if you are of working age but unfit to work.

You will find a list of the principal benefits for visually impaired people, registered or unregistered, on pages 131-136.

Registration should also act as a trigger to local services provided by your social services department. For example, you might be offered training in getting around or help in your home. In some cases you need to be registered to get help from voluntary agencies.

2.3 Do I have to register?

You do not have to register unless you want to. Some fear registration is a label - a sign of weakness, age, severe handicap or inability to cope. Some fear registration will mean they won't be able to go on living independently.

In fact it means none of these things. Registration does improve your chances of getting the help you need and we urge everyone with serious sight loss to consider it very carefully.

3 Coping day by day

3.1 How can I deal with my post? Or get information?

Few sighted people have any idea of the frustration of having to deal with paperwork when you can't see to read properly. Getting information is another huge challenge, whether you want to find out the times of local buses, the details of insurance policies or what's running in the 3.30.

The good news is that many information providers are now waking up to the needs of people who can't read ordinary print. So it pays to be pushy and ask people to send you information in a form you can read. For example:

● Some **banks and building societies** will send you statements in large print or braille, while others provide a service on the telephone. Some banks also provide cheque templates so you can write cheques more easily. If your bank is unhelpful, change your bank.

● **British Telecom,** and some of the **water** and **electricity** companies will send you bills in large print or braille. British Telecom and British Gas provide a talking bill service on the telephone.

● **The Inland Revenue** has produced some leaflets in large print, tape and braille, and others may follow. The **Benefits Agency** has many of its leaflets in large print and runs telephone help lines.

● **Insurance companies** have been slow to meet the needs but it's worth asking for your

Midland Bank, among others, produces a range of customer information in large print, tape and braille

bills and policies in large print, braille or on the telephone.

- Your **local council** should send you information or write to you in whatever form you need (though not all do as yet). Some local councils have large print, tape or braille guides to local services.

- **Personal correspondence** can be more difficult. Ask your family and friends to write to you using a thick-nibbed pen (if this helps you) or to put letters onto tape. Write your own letters with a big pen using a writing frame to guide you, or tape your letters, or learn to touch type.

- If you still need help with your post and have no family or friends to help, contact your local society for the blind and ask if they could find you a **volunteer reader**. If you are in a job and need help to read your paperwork, contact your local Jobcentre and ask about the 'Access to Work' scheme. This government-funded scheme enables you to employ a reader at your workplace.

If normal print is unreadable, getting information often means using new strategies which rely on the telephone, large print, radio and TV.

● If you can't see well enough to read a **telephone** book, you can use the free **Directory Enquiries** service. To find out about this service ring 0800-919195 (BT) or 0800-424194 (Mercury) - these calls are also free. **Talking Pages** (the talking equivalent of Yellow Pages) is a free service too. You can buy telephones with big, clear buttons which make them easier to use. (You can also buy telephones with other adaptations, for example amplifiers for people with hearing loss.) If you don't have a telephone and can't afford to install one, contact your social services department or Telephones for the Blind Fund to see if they can help with the cost (address 49 on page 130).

● The **radio**, especially local radio, is a useful source of information. There are a number of special programmes for people with sight problems including BBC Radio 4's 'In Touch' programme as well as local equivalents.

- **Big Print** is a weekly, national newspaper in large print. As well as news coverage it lists TV and radio programmes and has a giant crossword. Big Print is sent to subscribers by post (details are given on page 50). You will find additional information under questions 6.1, 6.2 and 6.3 on pages 77-82.

3.2 I find it very difficult to get out and about. Can anyone help?

The most important thing is not to lose all confidence. Although there are many hazards outside - such as uneven pavements and swiftly-moving traffic - care, caution, help and most of all training can help you retain the ability to move around safely.

Mobility training is invaluable. This can help you gain confidence in getting out and about and show you how to make the most of remaining sight as well as other senses. Your social services department may employ a specialist worker, so try ringing them to request mobility training. Be persistent - it's their duty to provide such help if you need it. If you have no luck, you should use the complaints procedure (see question 3.7).

Volunteer escorts are another possibility. Could you get someone - perhaps a friend or neighbour- to accompany you, particularly on complicated journeys? There's no harm in asking, and RNIB's booklet **How to guide a blind person** will give any companions confidence to help you. Or perhaps you could find a volunteer escort through your local society for the blind? (Ring RNIB Voluntary Agencies Link Unit to find out the telephone number of the one nearest you.) The British Red Cross and the WRVS can usually supply an escort for a difficult or unfamiliar route as long as you ask them in good time. Apply to your local branch: the address should be in your local 'phone book.

Some areas run special **taxi schemes**. The voluntary society and/or Citizens Advice Bureau should be able to tell you about these, as well as other **travel concessions** for visually impaired people and their escorts (see also question 5.6).

White canes can help you get around, as well as signal to others that you have a sight problem. There are different types, and ideally you should be shown how to use one by a rehabilitation worker. RNIB supplies white canes: details are given in the RNIB product guide **Mobility** (details on page 50).

A white cane is a simple and invaluable aid to getting out and about. But you do need training to get the best out of it.

Other useful equipment includes reflective Glo-discs which can be attached to clothing and make you highly visible to motorists. These can be obtained free from the Partially Sighted Society (address 34 on page 126) if you send a stamped addressed envelope.

Guide dogs are wonderful mobility aids, confidence-boosters and good companions too, but obviously need exercise and care. For more information contact the Guide Dogs for the Blind Association (address 21 on page 124) and ask them to send information (in large print, tape or braille) about becoming a guide dog owner.

If your journeys need to include **railway stations** or **coach stations**, telephone at least 24 hours in advance and ask for help. If you're travelling by **air**, mention your disability when you book your flight so arrangements can be made for you to board before other passengers. Increasingly, staff at stations and airports are being trained to help people with disabilities. **Tripscope** can give you advice and information on travel and transport (address 51 on page 130).

3.3 Is there anything I can do to make cooking and housework easier?

Running a home when you have little or no sight is hard work, especially if you are just losing your sight. However there are simple things you can do to make life easier and to give you back your confidence.

Most people with some sight benefit from an improved level of lighting in the home, especially on stairs and in the kitchen. In some eye conditions, though, glare is a problem, so experiment with lighting to find what works best for you. Another tip is to use colour contrast round your home. For example, chop potatoes on a dark chopping board rather than a cream-coloured one; put contrasting coloured tape round your power points so that you don't have to hunt for them.

A dark chopping board for light foods and vice versa can make cooking much simpler

If you have no useful sight, you'll need an approach based on touch and smell. Use your sense of smell to tell you whether food is going off, or whether your cakes, meat and so on are fully cooked. Keep everything in its place in the kitchen and elsewhere.

There are many products, such as easy-to-see timers and talking scales, which may help in the kitchen and home. Many products can be bought from RNIB by mail order, or at our resource centres in London, Stirling and Belfast where you can try them out first. Contact RNIB Customer Services for our free product guide **Daily living** (see page 50). You don't have to have special gadgets to survive, though!

With cooking, allow more time so you can work carefully. If safety is a concern, simple things can help. Use oven chips rather than a chip pan; frozen or ready-prepared vegetables which save having to chop. Use your back burners rather than the front ones; lighters rather than matches. Devise simple labels for foodstuffs, such as one rubber band round the tinned tomatoes, two on peaches and so on. Ask your family to record your favourite recipes on tape.

If it's hard to read the controls on your cooker, both gas and electricity boards can supply tactile adaptations - ask at your local showrooms. RNIB publishes a free booklet about labelling domestic equipment and produces simple, easy-to-feel labels (contact RNIB Customer Services, address 38 on page 127).

British Gas also has several schemes to help elderly and visually impaired people, such as an annual free gas safety check. Ask at the nearest showroom or district office for information and leaflets (available in clear print and on tape).

As for housework - it helps to take it slowly, for accidents usually happen when we rush. Try to work methodically, so you don't hoover the same bit of carpet twice! Keep your soap powders and equipment in the same place each time but, if you can, avoid storage space which is high up or difficult to reach. Discourage friends and relatives from moving anything in your home so you always know where to find things.

If your sight problem is severe, you should be able to get some help from your local authority, such as a home help or a specialist worker who can show you useful techniques for cooking and cleaning. If you'd like this, ring the social services department: ask about their community care services and rehabilitation teaching, and if they could send someone to assess your needs and give you advice.

If you get no response, you may wish to use the complaints procedure (see question 3.7). And you could also go on to try your local society for the blind. Some have resource centres where you can see a range of useful products. Some hold special classes and have staff who can help you in a variety of ways. RNIB Voluntary Agencies Link Unit (address 36 on page 126) can give you the address of the one nearest to you. We've listed some helpful publications at the end of this chapter.

3.4 Shopping is a problem for me. Have you any advice?

Large **supermarket** chains are becoming more responsive to customers these days. So why don't you start by telephoning your local supermarket, explaining your particular needs, and asking what they can do to help? Ask to speak to the store manager or someone in customer services.

Only a few companies do home deliveries, but most larger supermarkets should at least be able to provide someone to go round the shop with you. Have your shopping list to hand, and you can ask as you go about what is in each aisle, prices, special offers and so on. Alternatively, you could give them the list and they could collect the goods. Many supermarkets are happy to provide this kind of service, especially if you are a regular customer.

Small local shops where you are known are handy, although they tend to be more expensive. Ask if they can deliver your order - some still do. If you are lucky enough to have a milkman, ask if he delivers eggs, juice, bread or potatoes. This can save a lot of time and energy.

Shopping for clothes raises different problems. It's probably wise to take a friend or family member if you can - someone who will read labels and washing instructions for you, and tell you honestly how you look in that dress or jacket! It may also be worth considering whether you can do any shopping by mail order.

Coping with money can be stressful, especially now that notes are almost the same size. Try these ideas:

● Have a purse or wallet with several compartments so you can keep notes of different values separately. Flat coin holders are also useful.

● Ask your bank or post office to give you £5 and £10 notes only. This reduces the risk of confusion. You can also fold £5 notes one way and £10 notes a different way.

- Be prepared - try to anticipate roughly the cost and have slightly more than the amount needed at hand. (You're more likely to make mistakes when rushed.)

- Always have a combination of change in your pocket which adds up to £1.

- Get a template to help you fill in cheques (and your pension/allowance book) in the correct spaces. Most banks do them, so ask at your local branch; pension book templates are available from RNIB Customer Services (address 38 on page 127).

Simple templates can help you fill in cheques or pension books

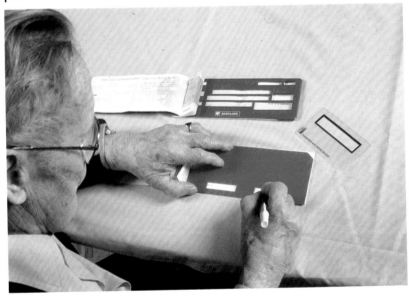

Transport to and from shops is perhaps another problem. Some areas have special schemes such as Dial-a-Ride. You can get information about such schemes from your local council or Tripscope (address 51 on page 130). If you need someone to help you to shop ask at your local Citizens Advice Bureau, or ring your local voluntary society for the blind to find out if there are any volunteers or local schemes which could help.

If you are **unable to shop at all** contact the social services department and ask for a visit from a social worker. Under the new community care laws you are entitled to help to enable you to live independently. Help with shopping is just one of the services you may be offered. Further information about care in your own home is given in question 3.6.

3.5 Are there any specific services for people from ethnic minorities?

People with little or no sight often lack information and advice. This is even more true if you are from an ethnic minority group and you may, therefore, miss out on essential services.

Although special help for people from ethnic minorities is thin on the ground, the following may be able to offer some help:

- **Association of Blind Asians** (address 5 on page 122). This offers information, advice and support in Asian languages, and provides mobility training and other services.

- **Organisation of Blind Afric-Caribbeans** (address 33 on page 126). This aims to provide information and advice to African and Caribbean people so they can fully benefit from existing services.

- **RNIB Development Officer for Ethnic Minorities** (address 36 on page 126), can refer you to speakers of your own language and can tell you where to get further help.

- **The hospital social worker or specialist worker in the social services department**. He may have links with interpreters. It is vital to have an interpreter if your English is not good enough to understand what your doctor is saying about your eye condition and treatment. You may also need an interpreter to discuss benefits you could claim.

● RNIB publishes a tape version of **Your Benefit** (see page 75), a guide to benefits for blind and partially sighted people, in several Asian and other languages. The **RNIB Talking Book Service** offers taped books in Asian languages and Welsh (address 45 on page 129).

3.6 **I've heard a lot about community care. What does it mean for me?**

The idea behind community care is that people should be given the help they need to live as independently as possible, ideally in their own homes. Social services departments are responsible for arranging services from a variety of sources - private, voluntary and public sector - to meet individual needs.

People with severe sight problems are entitled to an assessment of their needs for services, to include:

● help in the home

● getting around

● personal care

- finances/benefits

- accommodation

- leisure and employment

- social work support

- day centres

- adaptations or special equipment

- help with telephone rental

- residential or nursing home care if you can't live in your own home.

Your local authority must publish information about their assessment system, and the information should be available in suitable formats and languages. The system will differ from one place to another. If you request an assessment:

- You should be given the opportunity to state your opinion about the services required to meet your needs;

- Your carer (if you have one) should also be

able to state his or her views about their own needs;

- You should receive a letter - in a form and language you can read - giving you the result of the assessment;

- Local authorities are able to make a charge for services, provided the charge is reasonable. They should first ensure you are receiving all the benefits you are entitled to.

It is often easier to get help from your social services department if you are registered as blind or partially sighted - though this is by no means essential. (Registration is discussed in chapter 2 on pages 26-28.) But do **ask** for help if you need it. A little professional help can go a long way in keeping you independent and active.

3.7 I'm not happy with the services my local authority is providing. What can I do?

Every local authority must publish details of how to make complaints about the services provided. You should use this complaints procedure if you are not happy with any aspect of the service, including the result of the assessment, or the charges made for services.

There are three stages to the procedure:

● informal complaint to the service manager - most complaints are resolved at this stage;

● formal complaints should be registered through the complaints officer at the council;

● if the outcome is still not satisfactory, your complaint can be put before a review panel.

At all stages help should be available to you in putting forward your complaint, including having your complaint put into writing.

If you would like further information about assessment and complaints procedures, please contact RNIB Benefit Rights and Information Team (address 36 on page 126).

Further reading

BBC In Touch publications

Getting about safely. An In Touch Care Guide, 1991
(£1.75)

101 Practical hints for living with poor sight. An In Touch Care Guide, 1994
(£2.50)
(Both available in large print, braille or on tape from Broadcasting Support Services, PO Box 7, London W3 6XJ)

RNIB publications

A feeling for food (factsheet listing cookery books available in large print, braille or on tape)
(Free. Available in large print, braille or on tape)

A guide to public services in the home
(Free. Available in large print or braille)

A guide to microwave ovens
(Free. Available in large print or braille)

How to guide a blind person
(40p. Available in print or braille)

Labelling domestic equipment
(Free. Available in large print or braille)

Product guides including:

Clocks and watches
Daily living
Mobility
(Free. In large print, braille or on tape)

Running your own home
(40p. Available in print, tape or braille)

The cooker for you
(Free. Available in large print or braille)
(All the above RNIB publications are available from RNIB Customer Services, address 38 on page 127)

Other publications

Big Print (Big Print, PO Box 308, Warrington, Cheshire WA1 1JE, tel. 01925-242222)
(Weekly newspaper. £12.80 quarterly subscription)

Partial sight: how to cope by Mary Taylor. Robert Hale Ltd, 1993
(£6.99. In large print from bookshops)

4 Your home

4.1 My home is unsuitable and I need to move. What are my options?

Many types of housing are unsuitable for people with poor sight. However before you think about moving it is worth considering whether you could manage in your existing home if improvements could be made. Our answer to question 4.3 tells you about these and how to finance them.

If you have to move, then your options depend on whether you are buying your home or renting it from the local council or a private landlord.

Council tenants can consider any of the following:

● A **transfer** to more suitable property. Ask your local council's housing department about who gets priority. A sight problem may give you higher priority. The housing department will tell you how to apply for a transfer.

● An **exchange** of property. A number of schemes help people who wish to exchange property - your local housing department can explain these to you.

- A **cash incentive scheme** enables you to apply for a cash payment to buy your own home. You can also buy a share of a property and pay rent on the remaining part. Contact your council housing department for details.

If you are a **housing association** tenant there are similar transfer, exchange and cash incentive schemes to enable you to move. Contact your housing officer for information on these.

If you are a **private tenant**, you can apply to the council to be rehoused. Give the council supporting documents from your doctor, social worker or employer as these may improve your chances. You will need to go on a waiting list.

If your home is unsuitable because of the landlord's neglect, contact the local council's environmental health department. This department has legal powers to require landlords to do repairs. However, your landlord cannot be compelled to make adaptations to the property for you. If you are unclear about your rights, seek advice from a Citizens Advice Bureau or Housing Advice Centre.

If you **own your property** (or are buying it on a mortgage), you may need the help of sighted family or friends to move house. Selling a home, buying a new one, dealing with solicitors, estate agents and mortgage lenders is a minefield - the more so if you can't read documents easily or assess a new property. If you don't have family or friends to help, ask the Citizens Advice Bureau or your local society for the blind if they can find a helper for you.

Before visiting new properties, think carefully about the things that are important to you. You may need a home which is in excellent condition so maintenance is easy. You may prefer a home with no garden, or one without stairs. Easy access to shops, transport and a doctor may be important. Do ask estate agents and the home owner about things which are not necessarily obvious like noise from the neighbours, heating costs or what the street lighting is like. And, if you are buying a property, make sure you get a full structural survey first. Few things are worse than moving to your dream home only to find the building is subsiding.

Moving house can be a very fraught business for anyone with sight problems. If you need advice on any aspect of housing, get in touch with

RNIB's Housing Service (address 40 on page 128). Advice is free and we can help you on the telephone or write to you in large print, tape or braille.

4.2 I like to be independent at home but it would be good to have help in an emergency. Is there anything I can do?

You have two options here - either to move house to a more supportive type of housing, or to put an emergency alarm system into your current home.

If you are willing to move house, you can choose from sheltered housing, supportive housing, almshouses and special schemes for disabled or visually impaired people.

● **Sheltered housing** usually offers you a small flat or bedsit in a complex with a resident warden. You can summon the warden in an emergency using an alarm system. Generally the warden keeps an eye on residents anyway. For details of sheltered housing in your area contact your local council housing department, a Housing Advice Centre or Citizens Advice Bureau.

- **Supportive housing** offers you an element of care in your home such as cleaning and simple cooking. The Abbeyfield Society is the largest provider (address 1 on page 122).

- **Almshouses** may provide the kind of support you need, though some schemes are restricted to certain types of applicants. For information contact the Alms House Association (address 4 on page 122).

- **Special schemes** include housing for disabled people (meaning, usually, people who use wheelchairs) and housing and hostels specially designed or adapted for visually impaired people. There isn't enough housing in either of these categories, but if you'd like information, contact your local council housing department or RNIB's Housing Service (address 40 on page 128).

If you prefer to stay put in your present home, then you should consider an **emergency alarm system**. These use telephone technology to enable you to summon help in an emergency. You simply press a large button on the telephone or a remote control which you can carry in a pocket or on a chain round your neck. To find out more about these, contact Help the Aged, Community Alarms Department (address 22 on page 124).

| 4.3 | **Can I get help towards the cost of improving my home?** |

Many people with poor sight would benefit from simple improvements to their homes. For example, a ramp can replace difficult steps; heating and lighting controls can be adapted to make them easier to use; safety features such as grab rails can be installed in your bathroom. For advice about useful gadgets and adaptations, contact the Disabled Living Foundation or RNIB Housing Service (addresses 19 and 40 on pages 124 and 128).

If you can't afford these improvements, you can apply for several types of grants from your local council's housing department. These are:

- **Renovation Grants** - for owner-occupiers whose homes lack basic amenities (such as an inside toilet) or which need major structural repair.

- **Disabled Facilities Grants** - available to disabled tenants and owner-occupiers to adapt their homes so they can manage independently. For example grants can pay for improving access to your home or providing suitable bathroom and kitchen facilities. However you need to be registered as disabled, blind or partially sighted, or eligible to be registered, to get these grants. Contact your social services department to find out whether you could be registered.

- **Minor work assistance** - this is for people on income-related benefits and is mainly for those over 60 (owner-occupiers and tenants). The grants are available for minor repairs, for help with insulation, or for adapting properties if an elderly person is coming to live with you. Please note these grants are discretionary, so the local council can decide whether or not to help you. Contact your local housing department, a Housing Advice Centre, or RNIB's Housing Service for information.

● **Care and Repair** coordinates agencies which help with home improvements. There are agencies in most parts of the UK. Care and Repair's address is 13 on page 123 or you can get information from your local council's housing department.

4.4 I am about to be made homeless. Can anyone help me?

Local councils have a duty to make sure homeless people have somewhere to live. But you must show that you are in priority need and did not make yourself intentionally homeless. You could be counted as a priority if you have serious sight problems but councils vary on this. You are also regarded as a priority if you are over 60, or if someone you live with is over 60, or if you have dependent children, or are homeless because of fire, flood or other emergency. Contact the council's housing department.

If you are in any doubt about your legal rights to be rehoused contact a Citizens Advice Bureau or Housing Advice Centre. Alternatively, contact RNIB's Housing Service which can act as an advocate on your behalf (address 40 on page 128).

4.5 How do I find a suitable residential care home?

Before you think about moving into a home, it really is worth exploring the alternatives. It may be possible to stay in your own home with support, or perhaps sheltered housing could meet your needs (see question 4.2). Giving up your own home is a big step to take, so we suggest you discuss it with a professional adviser first. Contact your local social services department and ask to see a social worker who can assess your needs. She can also tell you about supported housing and homes in your area.

If residential care does seem the answer, there are many homes to choose from. Some are run by local councils, some by voluntary bodies (such as RNIB) and others by private owners. All will provide meals, help with personal care (such as bathing, dressing), shopping and so on. Nursing homes have to provide 24-hour nursing cover in addition to these services and may be more suitable if you are very disabled or ill.

The standards in homes vary widely. Many are excellent but others still have shared rooms or are rather inflexible about meal times or visitors. Some have awkward buildings with no lifts; some are in isolated places with no transport. It pays to be clued up about what to look for. Age Concern publishes a helpful factsheet 'Finding residential and nursing home accommodation' (address 3 on page 122).

You will need to visit the homes in person (take someone with you) to discuss their suitability for your needs. When you've found a likely place,

Residential care at its best should offer not just meals and care but also the opportunity to keep up your hobbies – and even learn new ones

arrange a trial stay of at least a month before you commit yourself and give up your own home. You can really only judge a home by staying there.

If you are worried about paying fees, please turn to question 5.5 on page 71.

Further reading

Department of Environment publications

House renovation grants. Department of Environment
(Free. Available in print from RNIB Housing Service, address 40 on page 128)

Your home in retirement: housing advice for older people. Department of Environment
(Free. Available in print from RNIB Housing Service, address 40 on page 128)

Age Concern publications

Finding residential and nursing home accommodation (Factsheet 29)

Older home owners: financial help with repairs (Factsheet 13)
(Up to five are free, but please send SAE. Available in print)

Housing options for older people, by David Bookbinder. Age Concern. Revised edition 1991
(£4.95. Available in print. These factsheets and books are available from Age Concern, address 3 on page 122)

5 Money matters

This section does not attempt to cover every aspect of money matters that may concern you. Instead it is mainly about state benefits that you may be entitled to. Our reason for narrowing the focus here is that many people with sight problems are on low incomes. Yet sight problems always bring higher costs - for example using taxis instead of buses. So, if you're on a low income it really is worth claiming even if you are not sure that you will get anything. These benefits are yours by right - you will not be asking for charity.

It is impossible to cover every situation here, but the questions in this section are among those most often asked. For more information, and advice relating to your own particular situation, the following may be helpful:

● **Benefits Agency Benefits Enquiry Line** - telephone 0800-882200 (freephone). Staff can answer queries (you don't need to give your name) and accept claims for some benefits over the telephone. They can send you part-completed claim forms in large print or braille.

- **RNIB Benefit Rights and Information Team** - 0171-388 1266 - can give you confidential individual advice and information. They also publish **Your Benefit** - a guide to benefits for visually impaired people - in large print, braille, Moon and on disk and tape (and in translation too - see page 75).

- **Action for Blind People** - 0171-732 8771 can provide information and publications.

- Your local **Benefits Agency** office (this used to be known as the 'social security' office) - should provide claim forms and a visiting officer if you ask for one.

- Your local **Citizens Advice Bureau** or **Law Centre** - can give you confidential individual advice and help with claims.

- Your **social worker**, or rehabilitation worker, if you have one, or an **advice worker** in your **local social services department** can give information.

On page 131 we have included a short guide to benefits for visually impaired people. You may also find this useful as an initial guide.

Please note that some of the benefits referred to here are available only to people who have registered their sight problem. You can read all about registration in chapter 2 on pages 26 to 28.

5.1	**What extra benefits - if any - are available to visually impaired people? How do I claim them?**

Unfortunately there's no such thing as a pension or allowance specifically for visually impaired people. You are, however, entitled to an extra income tax allowance if you are registered blind. Both blind and partially sighted adults and children, whether registered or not, can claim **Disability Living Allowance** (if you are under 66) or **Attendance Allowance** (if you are 66 or over).

These benefits are intended to help with extra costs arising from your disability. They are tax-free, and paid regardless of income, savings, wages, or other benefits you get. Payment of either allowance may result in other benefits too, such as a carers allowance or a higher rate of Income Support (if you get it).

Attendance Allowance is paid for extra personal care needed. Many people don't know about it, but RNIB Benefit Rights and Information Team suggest that all blind and partially sighted pensioners make a claim.

Disability Living Allowance is paid if you need some help getting around outdoors, or help with personal care such as reading your post or cooking a main meal. You can claim either or both the mobility and care parts of the allowance, and RNIB recommends all visually impaired people under 66 make a claim.

You can get claim forms for these allowances by contacting your local **Benefits Agency** office or telephoning the Benefits Enquiry Line (see page 63). You can ask for help to complete the form either by telephone or by home visit.

For more information, or if you want to appeal (this must be done within three months), telephone the Benefits Enquiry Line or RNIB Benefit Rights and Information Team (see page 64).

5.2 What financial help is available to people of working age?

If you are of working age, you may be entitled to claim some of the following benefits:

- **Income Support** - a weekly means-tested cash benefit. You may be able to claim this if you (or your partner, if you have one) work less than 16 hours a week. You may well be entitled to additional premiums. Income Support also has valuable 'fringe' benefits such as free NHS prescriptions and dental treatment.

- **Housing Benefit** - to help with rent payments. It is means-tested, so savings and income will be assessed, but you can get Housing Benefit even if your income is too high for Income Support.

- **Council Tax Benefit** - up to 100 per cent discount if your income is low, and a reduction if you live alone and/or your home has been specially adapted.

- **Severe Disablement Allowance** - a non-taxable, non-means-tested benefit payable if you are unable to work (though you are allowed to do a small amount of 'therapeutic work').

- **Invalidity Benefit** - a non-taxable, non-means-tested benefit, payable if you are unable to work (though you are allowed to do a small amount of 'therapeutic work'). This is higher than Severe Disablement Allowance, but you must have sufficient National Insurance contributions.

In April 1995 this benefit will be replaced by **Incapacity Benefit**. This is not means-tested but is taxable. Contact any of the agencies on pages 63-64 for further details.

● **Disability Working Allowance** - 'tops up' your income if you are working 16 hours or more a week, but your disability limits your earnings. It is means-tested. Seek advice before claiming.

● **Disability Living Allowance** - can be claimed in addition to other benefits. It is based on help you need with personal care and/or getting around outdoors and it is not means-tested.

● **Blind Person's Tax Allowance** - an additional personal income tax allowance, available to registered blind people. This allowance can be transferred to your partner, if you have one.

For more details about these benefits and how you can claim them contact an organisation listed on pages 63-64.

5.3 What financial help is available for people over retirement age?

If you are over statutory retirement age (60 for women, 65 for men) you may be entitled to some or all of the following benefits in addition to your State Retirement Pension:

- **Income Support** - a weekly means-tested cash benefit. This may be claimed if your income is below a certain level and you and your partner's savings are less than £8,000. You may be entitled to additional premiums.

- **Housing Benefit** - to help with rent payments. It is means-tested so your savings and income will be assessed, but you can get Housing Benefit even if your income is too high for Income Support.

- **Council Tax Benefit** - up to 100 per cent discount if your income is low, and a reduction if you live alone and/or your home has been specially adapted.

- **Attendance Allowance** - can be claimed in addition to any other benefits you get. It is based on help needed for personal care such as reading your post or getting round safely.

You can claim even if you live alone and it is not means-tested.

- **Disability Living Allowance** - can be claimed up to the age of 66 - see question 5.1 for details.

- **Blind Person's Tax Allowance** - an additional personal income tax allowance available to registered blind people. It can be transferred to your partner, if you have one.

For more details about these benefits and how you can claim them contact an organisation listed on pages 63-64.

5.4   Do carers get financial help?

If you are looking after someone, you may be entitled to a benefit called **Invalid Care Allowance**. You must be of working age, earn less than £50 weekly and care for someone for more than 35 hours a week. The person cared for must be receiving Attendance Allowance or the middle or higher rate care component of Disability Living Allowance.

This benefit is quite complex so it is wise to seek individual advice before claiming. Contact RNIB Benefit Rights and Information Team, your local Citizens Advice Bureau, or the Benefits Enquiry Line (see pages 63-64) for more information.

5.5 Can I get money towards the fees of a residential home?

Quite possibly - it all depends on your circumstances. If you were in the home before April 1993 you may be entitled to help with fees through Income Support ('preserved rights').

If you moved to the home after April 1993 or are now considering it, you may be able to get financial help through an Income Support residential allowance and through the local council social services department. However, social services will want to ensure that you need the type of care you are getting and that it is their obligation to help.

Check your position before moving into a home. Ask the local social services department for information. Age Concern England (address 3 on page 122) produce a helpful leaflet on residential care and you can also get information from the Benefits Enquiry Line and Counsel and Care (address 16 on page 123).

5.6 Can I get help with travel costs?

If you are registered blind or partially sighted, you may be entitled to some local and national travel concessions including:

- **British Rail** travel concessions including the **Disabled Persons Railcard**. Ask at your nearest mainline British Rail station, or contact RNIB/GDBA Mobility Unit (address 36 on page 126).

- **Local travel concessions** - ask your social services department for details of bus permit schemes, taxi cards etc.

- **Orange Badge scheme** - registered blind people are entitled to car parking concessions under this scheme (the car doesn't need to be yours). Contact your social services department for information.

- **Fares to work** - if you are unable to use public transport to get to work, you may get help with costs of alternative transport through the 'Access to Work' scheme. Ask at the local Jobcentre.

- **Air travel** - on most UK domestic flights a blind person and escort can travel for one full fare, if your journey is for business, education or medical reasons.

5.7 Can I get help towards housing and council tax bills?

You might be able to get considerable help towards housing costs.

- If you are on Income Support and pay rent, you should claim your full rent through **Housing Benefit**. Contact your council for information about Housing Benefit.

- You may still be able to claim Housing Benefit even if you work over 16 hours weekly, and/or your income is too high for Income Support.

- A **higher rate** of Housing Benefit may be paid if you are registered blind and/or you receive Disabled Living Allowance or Attendance Allowance. Contact the Housing Benefit section of your local council for a claim form.

- If you have a mortgage or home improvement loan and are on Income Support, it should be calculated to cover all or part of the weekly interest you pay.

Council tax is complicated, but there are three main ways you can get your bill reduced. These are:

- a 100 per cent rebate - **Council Tax Benefit** - if you are on Income Support or a low income;

- a 25 per cent discount if you live alone, regardless of income;

- a reduction if your home has been adapted for you as a disabled person.

For more information contact your local council. RNIB Benefit Rights and Information Team (see page 64) can give you confidential advice.

5.8 I have just got a large bill that I am unable to pay. Can anyone help?

You can get advice about money - including help with prioritising and negotiating payments -

from your local Citizens Advice Bureau, Money Advice Centre or National Debtline (address 29 on page 125). They also advise on debt management.

There are some charities which give grants to visually impaired people in particularly difficult circumstances. You could contact RNIB's Grants and Information Officer (address 36 on page 126) for information about charitable sources of help.

Further reading

RNIB publications

Your benefit. RNIB, annual (£3.00/£1.00 to claimants. A new edition is published each April. Available in large print, braille or on tape from RNIB Customer Services, address 38 on page 127. Also available on tape in several minority languages)

RNIB factsheets

RNIB Benefit Rights and Information Team produces a number of free factsheets on benefits and other services. Contact them at address 36 on page 126.

Other publications

Action for Blind People factsheets on benefits, pensions and grants for visually impaired people
(Free. Available in large print, braille and on tape. Send SAE for a full list of factsheets to Action for Blind People, address 2 on page 122)

The disability rights handbook. Disability Alliance, annual
(£6.95 or £5.00 for people on benefit. Available in print from Disability Alliance, address 17 on page 124)

Guide to grants for individuals in need, edited by P Brown and D Casson. The Directory of Social Change, 1994
(£15.96. Bi-annual publication. Available in print)

Social security benefits: a guide for blind and partially sighted people (ref FB19).
Benefits Agency
(Free booklet. Available in large print and tape from your local Benefits Agency office)

6 Keeping up your reading and other interests

6.1 What is available in large print? Where can I get it?

Most visually impaired people use print and there is a growing range of large print material to choose from - though by no means enough. As question 3.1 (see page 29) indicates, there is much more awareness of the need for large print for everyday information. So you should be able to get your bills, bank statements and tax leaflets in large print. You may be able to get guides to local and national services in large print from your local library, Citizens Advice Bureau, local society for the blind, or resource centre for visually impaired people, if there is one nearby.

A number of publishers produce books, games, maps, religious publications, reference books and other materials in large print. RNIB Community Education Office (address 36 on page 126) can send you a list of who produces what and where to get it. Few large print books are stocked by bookshops, so you will probably need to get catalogues and order direct from publishers.

Public libraries are a good source of large print fiction and most carry catalogues of what is available. The National Library for the Blind (address 31 on page 125) has a selection of classics and other works. A catalogue is available on request and you can ask your public library to order these or other large print books. You could be entitled to home delivery if you can prove the need - ask the librarian about this.

You may also enjoy **Big Print** - a weekly newspaper which includes a review of national and international news as well as TV and radio listings and a giant crossword. It is available by post (details are given on page 91).

6.2 What is available on tape? Where can I find out more?

There is a growing amount of material on tape. It includes books, newspapers and magazines, specialist journals, study materials and other information.

Some leaflets covering essential information such as community care, guides to council tax, or fire safety, are available on tape. These are distributed free through agencies such as

Citizens Advice Bureaux, libraries, local societies for the blind, and talking newspapers.

Books on tape have always been popular. Your public library may have a collection and you can also buy these in some bookshops, though they can be expensive. A good source of listening material is RNIB Talking Book Service (address 45 on page 127) which supplies books by post on special cassettes and a machine with which to listen to them. These recordings cover all your favourite fiction, biography and other general interest titles. RNIB Cassette Library (address 38 on page 127) lends some fiction and a wide range of non-fiction. Calibre (address 12 on page 123) is another lending library of books recorded on standard cassettes.

If you would like to listen to taped versions of local or national newspapers and magazines contact Talking Newspapers Association of the UK (address 48 on page 130). You can receive local talking newspapers free if you are registered and many public libraries have a selection of newspapers and magazines on tape.

You can also get books or other printed material such as recipes, knitting patterns, instruction leaflets or study materials, specially recorded on tape. You can find out more about recording services as well as what is already available on tape from RNIB Customer Services (address 38 on page 127).

Some useful publications are listed at the end of this chapter on pages 90-93.

6.3 Is it worth learning braille? How do I set about it?

Braille is a system of raised dots which enables people to read and write by touch. It is certainly worth learning braille if print is impractical. Age is no barrier, for people in their 70s and 80s have successfully learnt it, though braille can be tricky if your fingertips have lost their sensitivity.

You can use braille for tasks such as labelling or noting phone numbers, as well as for reading books and other material. It is extremely useful at work, since it can be used on files, records and adapted computers.

Some social services departments provide braille teachers, but you may need to be persistent. You can also find out about local teachers from RNIB

Customer Services (address 38 on page 127). RNIB and others publish a range of braille teaching packs. Although best used with a teacher, some of these can also be used on their own. Contact RNIB Customer Services (address 38 on page 127) for information.

You can get a reasonable choice of material in braille, including magazines, leaflets, books, music, exam papers, even your bank statements.

Learning braille gives you access to books and magazines and a means to write your own information, such as address lists or favourite recipes

The largest publishers are RNIB and National Library for the Blind, the Scottish Braille Press, and the Torch Trust (addresses 38, 31, 46 and 50 on pages 125-130). The most widely read publications are the **Radio Times** and **TV Times**. You can get information about what is available in braille from RNIB Customer Services, which also supplies braillers and paper for brailling. Incidentally one benefit of reading braille is that you can send it by post free of charge.

6.4 What is Moon? How can I find out more about it?

Moon, like braille, is a system of reading and writing by touch. People whose fingers lack the sensitivity to read braille dots sometimes find Moon easier to learn. The system is based on raised lines, and many of its letter shapes are similar to print. Like braille, Moon can be used to label things.

Some social services departments provide Moon as well as braille teaching as part of their services for visually impaired people. If you can't get help this way, contact RNIB Customer Services (address 38 on page 127) who have a register of teachers, a Moon teaching pack and

Moon magazines and books. The National Library for the Blind (address 31 on page 125) has the largest collection of Moon books. However there is only a limited amount of material in this medium.

6.5 Can I keep doing active sport?

Losing your sight does not mean the end of your sporting life! Visually impaired people take part in many sports activities including cricket, athletics, sailing, skiing, water skiing, bowls, rambling, mountaineering, tandem riding, swimming - in fact almost everything! However, it's sensible to discuss your sports interests with your doctor first, and of course you must explain your sight condition to sports instructors.

If you belong to or wish to join an ordinary sports club you should be able to take part in a number of activities, although racquet sports might not be possible depending on your eye condition.

There are also sports clubs specifically for visually impaired people. A coordinating body called British Blind Sport (BBS) (address 9 on page 123) can tell you what is available in your area. BBS run 'Have a Go' days (to try out different sports), as well as selecting teams for international competition including the Paralympic Games. Another source of information about sport and other leisure activities is RNIB Leisure Service (address 36 on page 126). You may also find useful the **In Touch** handbook on sport and leisure (see page 93).

6.6   How can I keep up my hobbies?

If your sight loss is moderate, good lighting and low vision aids such as magnifiers (see page 19) can help a lot. But even if sight loss is severe you can still pursue many activities. Have a go - you won't know what you can do until you try!

You can get indoor games such as cards, dominoes, draughts, chess, Scrabble and Monopoly, in forms adapted for people with sight loss. (These can be played with people who are sighted too.) There are, for example, large print playing cards as well as cards embossed with braille or Moon. RNIB Customer Services (address 38 on page 127) can send you a free product guide giving details of these.

A large print and braille version of 'Monopoly' can be played by everyone

Many people successfully pursue art and craft activities - at home or in classes or workshops. For example, you can continue to enjoy your knitting or crocheting using large print, tape or braille patterns. You can also enjoy visual arts. There are 'Art to Share' groups around the country and the Living Paintings Trust (address 25 on page 125) can lend you (free) tactile versions of famous paintings, together with taped commentaries.

Some art and museum exhibitions, and buildings of interest make special provision.

There are for example taped guides to some cathedrals, English Heritage, and National Trust sites. The National Trust (address 32 on page 126) can send you information about sites which have guides in large print, braille and/or tape. If you're a theatre lover, look out for theatres with audio description (spoken commentaries about the action on stage). RNIB Leisure Service can tell you more about these.

Perhaps you enjoy watching or doing drama, dance and music activities? To find out more about these and all other leisure pursuits and organisations, contact RNIB Leisure Service which can offer information and a range of publications (address 36 on page 126).

6.7 How can I cope with my garden?

Gardening is a popular activity, and many people with sight problems are extremely successful at it.

Even if you feel frustrated at the beginning, and perhaps have to find new ways of working, repeated practice and a bit of advice from the experts are the keys to success.

You can get detailed information and advice from:

- **Horticultural Therapy** (address 24 on page 124), a national organisation which has developed many gardening opportunities for people with sight loss. They publish the quarterly magazine **Come Gardening** (on cassette, in braille or in Moon) and subscribers have free use of the cassette library. This organisation runs the **Advisory Committee for Blind Gardeners** which organises gardening weekends and answers any queries.

- **RNIB Leisure Service** (address 36 on page  126) can send you a free gardening information pack. It also publishes **Gardening without sight** which is a practical guide to all garden tasks (see page 92).

This couple enjoy scented plants in raised flower beds

6.8 Have you any advice about holidays?

Depending on your wishes and needs, there are a number of different options to consider:

- **Holiday hotels** - some cater specifically for visually impaired people - alone or with sighted companions. Most are run by voluntary organisations, including RNIB. Contact RNIB Hotels and Holiday Service for a full list.

- **Group holidays** - these are generally organised by voluntary societies or local authorities, and provide transport, accommodation and entertainment. Many are in the UK, but some societies arrange foreign holidays also.

- **Activity holidays** - these are good if you are looking for something challenging such as hill climbing or sailing. There are activity centres which cater specially for people with disabilities. The Guide Dogs Adventure Group (address 21 on page 124) has holidays in the UK and abroad in activities ranging from skiing to listening to bird song. And you don't have to own a guide dog to join in!

- **Residential courses** - these are offered in a huge range of subjects including music, photography, wine tasting, sculpture, aromatherapy and natural history.

- **Holiday hotels abroad** - the BBC In Touch Care Guide on travel lists hotels and centres abroad for visitors with impaired sight.

- **Residential homes for visually impaired people** - some take short-stay holiday guests, some on a self-catering basis. They are usually very well equipped.

To find out more... RNIB Leisure Service (address 36 on page 126) can give you fuller information and send you a holiday information pack. The Holiday Care Service (address 23 on page 124) can give individual advice (including getting help with the cost of holidays) and send you a large print information leaflet. For information about travel concessions see question 5.6. And finally, we've listed some useful publications below.

Further reading

Print and its alternatives

RNIB leaflets

Information on learning braille for adults
Information on learning braille for children and teenagers
Introducing Moon
Some sources of large print material
(These are free in large print from RNIB Customer Services, address 38 on page 127)

Big Print (Big Print, PO Box 308, Warrington, Cheshire WA1 1JE, tel. 01925-242222)
(Weekly newspaper. £12.80 quarterly.)

Guide to taped services for the handicapped. Talking Newspaper Association, annual
(£5.00. Available in large print, braille or on tape from Talking Newspaper Association, address 48 on page 130)

The pleasures of listening. An In Touch Care Guide. Revised edition 1992
(£1.95. Available in large print, braille or on tape from Broadcasting Support Services, PO Box 7, London W3 6XJ)

Leisure

RNIB publications

Discovering museums: a guide to museums in the UK for blind and partially sighted people. RNIB/HMSO, 1993
(£9.95)

Discovering sports venues: a visually impaired person's guide to some favourite spectator sports. 1993
(£2.50)

Games and puzzles (Product Guide)
(Free)

Gardening without sight, by Kathleen Fleet,
1989
(£2.50)
(All the above are available in large print,
braille or on tape from RNIB Customer
Services, address 38 on page 127)

BBC In Touch publications

Sport and leisure. An In Touch Care Guide,
1992
**Travel and holidays. An In Touch Care
Guide,** 1992
(Both £1.95 and available in large print,
braille or on tape from Broadcasting Support
Services, PO Box 7, London W3 6XJ)

Other publications

Holidays in the British Isles. RADAR
(£5.00)

Holidays and travel abroad. RADAR
(£3.50)
(Both the above are updated every year and
available in print from RADAR, address 35 on
page 126)

Nothing ventured: tales of disabled travellers. Rough Guides. 1992
(£7.99. Available in print from any bookshop)

7 Jobs and training

In the past, most people with sight problems who wanted to work did so in 'sheltered' employment. Although a small minority still earn a living that way, most visually impaired people in work now do many of the same jobs as fully sighted people. So, however limited your sight, you don't need to limit your job horizons.

There are a number of sources of help if you want to keep your current job, find a job or train for something new. These include:

Placing, Assessment and Counselling Teams (PACTs), which can identify individual needs and suggest training opportunities. They can be reached via your **Jobcentre**;

RNIB Employment Network, which offers services including assessment, training, advice, information and practical help. It has six regional teams (all addresses under 39 on page 128).

Computers can be adapted for large print, braille or speech, enabling visually impaired people to do a very wide range of jobs

7.1 I'm finding my job very difficult because of my sight. Should I resign?

Almost certainly not, but you should seek specialist advice and practical assistance right away. There are many services available - such as adaptations to equipment, special technical aids and reading assistance - which may enable you to continue doing the same job. These services are only available to you while you have a job, though.

The government's Access to Work scheme aims to provide the help you need to stay in (or get into) work. It covers:

- provision of special technical aids

- grants for adapting premises or equipment

- help with the costs of travel to work

- grants to enable you to pay for a reader or other support.

These services are provided at no cost to you or your employer.

To find out more, contact your nearest Jobcentre and ask for the Disability Employment Adviser or Placing, Assessment and Counselling Team (PACT). It is also worth contacting RNIB Employment Network (addresses 39 on page 128). A consultant from RNIB Employment Network can work on your behalf in negotiations with your employer and in helping you make best use of government schemes. If you decide in the end that you would benefit from a change of job or retraining, you can get detailed information and advice from RNIB Employment Network.

While you are discussing your future with these specialists, it may help to discuss your situation with a sympathetic colleague or trade union representative. It can be very stressful to have to cope with worsening eyesight and your job. Talking about your worries won't make them go away, but it does help.

7.2 What sort of jobs can people with poor sight do?

A huge range. There are visually impaired secretaries, solicitors, engineers, teachers, cycle mechanics, physiotherapists, gardeners,

computer programmers, social workers, counsellors, craft-workers, musicians, publicans, MPs, administrators... and many thousands more doing a wide range of jobs. Obviously there are some limitations; you can't drive buses or fly planes, for instance. On the other hand, new technology has opened up many fresh opportunities for people with little or no sight.

If you are interested in finding out more about possible options, get in touch with RNIB Employment Network (addresses 39 on page 128). RNIB also has an expanding library of careers information on tape.

7.3 Where can I get job training?

A good start is to get in touch with your local Placing, Assessment and Counselling Team (PACT) via your local Jobcentre, and RNIB Employment Network. They can tell you about job assessment, rehabilitation courses including mobility, and job training - both locally and further afield. Occupational psychologists employed by PACT or RNIB can undertake vocational assessment with you to help you decide on the best training.

If it seems appropriate you can go straight into a training course at your local college of further education, or elsewhere. In this case, RNIB's Employment Network and Student Support Service can provide practical support for both you and the local college to help you follow your chosen course.

Another option is to do a course at a specialist college where all the students have impaired sight and where the staff are trained to work with you. Specialist colleges offer a wide range of courses including business skills, computing, telephony, engineering, horticulture, braille and

Training in computer skills at an RNIB centre

craft work among other subjects. You can get advice about specialist colleges from any of the organisations listed on page 94.

Sometimes, if considered job-ready, visually impaired people are directed straight into Training for Work schemes provided through the local Training and Enterprise Council (TEC) or Local Enterprise Council (LEC) in Scotland.

If you don't feel ready to plunge into training courses, perhaps because your sight loss is very recent, you should first consider a short course at a rehabilitation centre. These courses are designed to guide you through your job options by providing assessment, training in relevant skills (such as mobility, job-seeking skills, braille) and advice about your next steps. RNIB runs two rehabilitation centres, Manor House in Torquay and Alwyn House in Fife (addresses under 42 on page 129).

If you would like more detail about job training and rehabilitation, you may find it useful to look at the BBC's **In Touch Handbook** (details on page 103.)

7.4 Can anyone help me set up my own business?

You should ring or visit your local PACT team at the Jobcentre to ask them about services offered by the Department of Employment to help small firms and homeworkers.

You can also get advice on all aspects of setting up a business from the small business specialists at RNIB Employment Network (addresses 39 on page 128). RNIB runs courses, can give advice on local authority funded home-working schemes and sheltered employment, and has an information library with material in tape, large print and braille.

You may also find helpful the Blind Business Association (address 7 on page 122) which provides a useful forum for exchanging ideas and experience.

There are pitfalls, but the good news is that more and more visually impaired people are setting up their own business, some very successfully.

7.5 I believe there is special equipment to help me at work. Where do I find out about it? Do I have to pay for it?

A wide range of special aids and adaptations to work equipment is available to working people who have little or no sight. Some of this equipment is quite basic - such as hand magnifiers or adjustable lighting - and some more complex, such as talking computers.

You can get details from the PACT team through your nearest Jobcentre. You can also contact RNIB Employment Network (addresses 39 on page 128): they will assess your requirements and make an application to the Department of Employment for the equipment you need to do your job. It's wise to stay in close contact, for sometimes there can be delays in the process.

You will not have to pay for any special equipment, nor will your employer. The costs are met by the government.

Further reading

RNIB publications

Employment matters: everything you need to know about finding and keeping a job! 1992

Get that job! A guide for visually handicapped job hunters. 1988

Working for you: new technology at work for visually handicapped people. 1991
(£1.00 each or £2.00 for all three booklets.)
Available in large print, braille or on tape
from RNIB Customer Services, address 38 on
page 127.

BBC In Touch publications

The In Touch Handbook, edited by Margaret
Ford and Thena Heshel. BBC, annual
(£17.95. Available in print, braille or on tape
from Broadcasting Support Services, PO Box 7,
London W3 6XJ)

8 Help for parents, children and young people

8.1 What help and advice is there for parents of children with impaired sight?

Finding out that your child has little or no sight can be a difficult experience. Most parents feel deeply shocked when they are first told, and are very concerned about the future. Nowadays, however, a sight problem should not hold your child back.

Help is available from a number of sources:

- **Health professionals** - include your GP, your child's health visitor, paediatrician, orthoptist and ophthalmologist. They each have a particular interest in your child's sight and development and your health visitor will be able to explain their different roles. If you are unclear about your child's eye condition, talk it through with your GP or with another professional.

- **The hospital social worker** - may be able to give you initial advice and point you towards other sources of help.

- **The social services department** - ask to see a specialist worker to advise you on local sources of help. Social services are legally obliged to devise an appropriate package of services for your family.

- **Local Education Authorities (LEAs)** - employ specialist teachers of visually impaired children. Don't wait until school age - ring the LEA and ask for an appointment with the specialist as soon as you know your child has a sight problem. You can discuss how best to develop your child's skills and confidence as well as educational opportunities.

- **Parents' support groups** - run by parents of visually impaired children, these are a good way for families to share experiences and information. To find out about groups in your area contact **Look** (address 26 on page 125). **Sense** (address 47 on page 130) runs a telephone befriending service for parents and carers of deafblind children. **Vision Aid** (address 52 on page 130) and **Eyeline** (address 20 on page 124) are support groups for parents offering national services. Both have a 24-hour helpline. There are also self-help groups for different eye conditions.

- **RNIB Education Information Service** (address 36 on page 126) - provides information and advice about child development, education, play and other issues. It has a wide range of leaflets and books for parents and teachers and can tell you about national and local services. It also publishes two magazines, **Visability** and **eye contact** for parents and others (details on page 117).

- **Where children have additional disabilities** - you may need to speak to several different experts. Two organisations you may find useful are **Sense** (address 47 on page 130) if your child has impaired hearing as well as sight, and **RNIB Education Information Service**, if your child has multiple disabilities.

| 8.2 | **Can we get financial help for our child?** |

Yes, your child may qualify for a benefit called **Disability Living Allowance.** If you can show that he needs substantially more attention or supervision than a sighted child of the same age, then he is likely to qualify. In addition to a payment for care needs, which can be claimed from birth, you can also claim a mobility part of the allowance - for help with getting around. The mobility part, however, can be claimed only for a child over five (you can claim from three months before his fifth birthday).

For more information, telephone the Benefits Enquiry Line (freephone 0800-882200), RNIB Benefit Rights and Information Team (address 36 on page 126) or visit your local Citizens Advice Bureau. You can get a claim pack from your local Benefits Agency office or the Benefits Enquiry Line, but it is always a good idea to seek informed advice before claiming.

8.3 How do we get the best education for our child?

To many parents, schooling must seem a daunting issue. But there is a lot of support available to help you choose the right schools and get the special support your child may need.

Your Local Education Authority (LEA) has a specialist teacher who will be able to discuss your child's needs and options with you. She can advise on local services and put you in touch with schools in your area. The RNIB Education Officer in your area can also provide advice and guidance.

Many visually impaired children attend the local primary or secondary school. These are sometimes referred to as 'mainstream' schools. Your child will join in ordinary classroom activities, possibly with additional support such as special equipment or the help of a non-teaching assistant. Some children's needs may be best met by a 'special school' where all the children have special needs and where staff have appropriate training. Parents often find it helpful to visit a few schools to see what is available in the local area. Your LEA will provide you with details.

Learning braille in an ordinary classroom

Your LEA also has to ensure that a full assessment of your child's needs is carried out. The assessment will highlight what special help your child will need, such as equipment or extra help in class. It will recommend what type of school will best meet his needs. You will be asked to contribute to this assessment.

Once the assessment is complete, a 'Statement of special educational needs', or 'Record' in Scotland, is usually written. This is a legally binding document which sets out what the LEA promises to provide for your child. The Statement/Record will be reviewed each year to check that it's up-to-date and accurate. RNIB Advocacy Service (address 37 on page 127) can help you prepare your contribution to the assessment and deal with any problems concerning Statements.

If you or your child are not happy with any aspect of his schooling, talk it over with your child's teacher first. If you feel you need more information or advice, contact the LEA Visual Impairment Service. If you are unhappy with the education your child receives, you can make an appeal to an impartial appeal panel. Your LEA can tell you about the appeal procedure. RNIB Advocacy Service can advise you how to make an appeal and help you to prepare your case.

For more information about education services in general, contact the RNIB Education Information Service (address 36 on page 126).

8.4 What opportunities are there in further and higher education?

The choices are wider now than ever before, so our advice is to shop around to find exactly what you're looking for. You can study most subjects in many places, provided you have the right entry requirements.

Many, though not all, mainstream colleges and universities cater for students with special needs. This means the college should have basic equipment such as a CCTV and adapted computers. The Special Needs Co-ordinator at the college will be able to discuss your individual needs and advise about the college facilities and sources of extra help. Several specialist colleges cater specifically for the needs of students with impaired sight and RNIB Student Support Service can provide more information about these.

You can get advice about your options from your local careers service and from RNIB. RNIB Student Support Service (address 44 on page 129), supported by colleagues in other parts of RNIB, brings together a comprehensive range of services including education, employment, library and reader services. These help students to gain access to further and higher education, training and jobs. Advisers offer a one-to-one service to students who do not have support services at college or university and they will act on your behalf where college support fails.

You may be entitled to extra financial help. If you receive a mandatory award from your Local Education Authority (LEA) or the Scottish

Education Department or Northern Ireland Education and Library Board, you may apply for the Disabled Students Allowance (DSA). When you apply for a grant, indicate that you have a disability and would like more information about DSA. RNIB Student Support Service (address 44 on page 129) will be happy to provide more information and help with this.

8.5 Are there any special leisure facilities for children with impaired sight?

Play is children's most important leisure activity. Choose toys which have a variety of textures, make a noise or are brightly coloured. These can help your child to develop her residual vision, skills and senses in a relaxed, fun way. Many toys available from high street shops are useful. RNIB produces a free catalogue which lists toys suitable for all ages, from babies to adults (details on page 117). Your local toy library may also be a useful resource: contact the National Association of Toy and Leisure Libraries for details of the nearest (address 27 on page 125).

Several organisations in your area will run leisure activities which are safe and fun for blind and partially sighted children. Your local society for the blind or parent support group will be able to put you in touch with events and playschemes in your area. RNIB Education Information Service can provide useful names and addresses. **Eye contact** and **Visability** magazines publicise leisure events and ideas throughout the year (details on page 117).

British Blind Sport (address 9 on page 123) organises sports clubs and fun days for visually impaired children and will be able to advise you about facilities in your area. RNIB Leisure Service (address 36 on page 126) provides details of other organisations in your area.

Holidays give children the opportunity to explore new skills and meet children from other

Learning rock - climbing on an RNIB Vacation Scheme

areas. Children who attend mainstream schools and colleges may enjoy one of RNIB's Vacation Schemes. They meet other children with impaired sight and enjoy all sorts of challenging and fun activities from water sports to art. RNIB also offers weekend breaks for the whole family, providing entertainment for the children and information and support for the parents. For details of both schemes, contact RNIB Education Information Service (address 36 on page 126).

8.6 Is there any help for parents who are blind or partially sighted?

Most visually impaired parents have brought up children with great success. Obviously some practical difficulties arise, but it is other parents who are in the best position to offer support and advice.

Useful sources of help include:

● The **National Childbirth Trust** runs **ParentAbility**, a network which supports pregnancy and parenthood for people with disabilities. It has a national contact register and publishes a newsletter in print and tape. The National Childbirth Trust also provides information on labour, breastfeeding, support services and local antenatal and postnatal groups. (Address 28 on page 125.)

- RNIB publishes a monthly braille magazine **You and your child** with articles on pregnancy and child care. Contact RNIB Customer Services (address 38 on page 127) for details. They can also tell you about other tape, braille and large print publications for parents.

- **Disability Network** produces tape versions of some useful catalogues - Mothercare, Boots 'Baby and child' and the Early Learning Centre. They can also provide other information to visually impaired parents. Contact them at address 18 on page 124.

Further reading

RNIB publications

Choices for children: educational opportunities for visually impaired children and young people, 1993
(50p. Available in print or on tape)

Early years series:
Look and touch: play activities and toys for children with visual impairments, 1994
(£2.00. Available in print)

Helping your visually impaired child: an introduction to key services, 1994
(£1.50. Available in print or on tape)

The world in our hands
A series of five videos with booklets for parents of blind babies and pre-school children and professionals who work with them.

(Each video and booklet is £17.00; booklet only £2.00; complete set of five videos and booklets £75.00)

(All the above are available from RNIB Customer Services, address 38 on page 127)

Information and factsheets

100 popular toys and games for blind and partially sighted children (12-page catalogue)

Information pack for visually impaired children with additional disabilities

RNIB Student Support Service

Social security benefits for visually impaired children
(All the above are free and available in print from RNIB Education Information Service, address 36 on page 126)

Magazines

eye contact (termly magazine about the education of visually impaired children who have additional learning difficulties - for parents and professionals)

Visability (termly magazine about the education of visually impaired children - for parents and professionals)

(Each magazine costs £6.00 a year and is available in print from RNIB Education Information Service, address 36 on page 126.)

Addresses

Information and support groups

This list includes some of the many groups which provide information about different eye conditions. If you have an eye condition which is not listed here and would like to know if there is an organisation which can help you, please contact RNIB Ophthalmic Advisory Service (address 36 on page 126).

There are many other groups you can join. Some are special interest groups (eg for computer users), others have a broader remit, such as the National Federation of the Blind which campaigns on behalf of visually impaired people. Contact RNIB (address 36, page 126) for a list of these groups.

Albinism: The Albino Fellowship, 16 Neward Crescent, Prestwick KA9 2JB.   01292-703396

Behçet's Syndrome: Behçet's Syndrome Society, 3 Church Close, Lambourne, Newbury, Berkshire RG16 7PU.   01488-71116

Diabetic Retinopathy: National Diabetic Retinopathy Network, 7 Shore Close, Hampton, Middlesex TW12 3XS.   0181-941 5821 (evenings)

British Diabetic Association, 10 Queen Anne Street, London W1M 0BD.   0171-323 1531

Dystonia: Dystonia Society, Omnibus Workspace, 41 North Road, London N7 9DP. 0171-700 4594

Glaucoma: International Glaucoma Association, King's College Hospital, Denmark Hill, London SE5 9RS.   0171-737 3265

Laurence-Moon-Bardet-Biedl: L-M-B-B Society, 26 Lodge Causeway, Fishponds, Bristol BS16 3JA. 01179-654154

Leber's Optic Neuropathy: Leber's Optic Neuropathy Trust, 13 Palmar Road, Maidstone, Kent ME16 ODL.   01622-751025

Lupus: Lupus UK, PO Box 999, Romford, Essex RM1 1DW.   01708-731251

Macular Degeneration: Macular Disease Society, Central Office, PO Box 268, Weybridge, Surrey KT13 OYW.   01932-829331

Marfan Syndrome: Marfan Association UK, 6 Queen's Road, Farnborough, Hampshire GU14 6DH.   01252-547441

Nystagmus: Nystagmus Action Group (NAG), 43 Gordonbrook Road, London SE4 1JA. 0181-690 6679

Retinitis Pigmentosa: British Retinitis Pigmentosa Society, PO Box 350, Buckingham MK18 5EL.   01280-860363

Retinoblastoma: Retinoblastoma Society, c/o Academic Dept of Paediatric Oncology, St Bartholomew's Hospital, West Smithfield, London EC1A 7BE.   0171-600 3309 (answerphone 4 days a week, staffed Wednesday only)

Toxoplasmosis: The Toxoplasmosis Trust, Room 26, 61-71 Collier Street, London N1 9BE. 0171-713 0663 (0171-713 0599 Helpline)

Usher Syndrome: Sense Usher Services, 11-13 Clifton Terrace, Finsbury Park, London N4 3SR. 0171-272 7774

Other addresses

1. **Abbeyfield Society,** Abbeyfield House, 53 Victoria Street, St Albans, Herts AL1 3UW. 01727-857536

2. **Action for Blind People,** 14/16 Verney Road, London SE16 3DZ.   0171-732 8771

3. **Age Concern England,** Astral House, 1268 London Road, London SW16 4EJ. 0181-679 8000

4. **Alms House Association,** Billingbear Lodge, Wokingham, Berkshire RG11 5RU. 01344-52922

5. **Association of Blind Asians,** 322 Upper Street, London N1 2XQ.   0171-226 1950

6. **Benefits Agency Benefits Enquiry Line.** 0800-882200 (freephone)

7. **Blind Business Association,** The Secretary, 98 Aldborough Road, Upminster, Essex RM14 2RS.   01708-458475

8. **British Association for Counselling,** 1 Regent Place, Rugby CV21 2PJ. 01788-578328

9. **British Blind Sport,** 67 Albert Street, Rugby CV21 2SN. 01788-536142

10. **British Red Cross,** 9 Grosvenor Crescent, London SW1X 7EE. 0171-235 5454

11. **British Wireless for the Blind Fund,** 34 New Road, Chatham, Kent ME4 4QR. 01634-832501

12. **Calibre,** Aylesbury, Buckinghamshire HP22 5XQ. 01296-432339 or 81211

13. **Care and Repair,** Castle House, Kirtley Drive, Nottingham NG7 1 LD. 01159-744091

14. **Carers National Association,** 20-25 Glasshouse Yard, London EC1A 4JS. 0171-490 8898 (advice line between 1pm and 4pm). 0171-490 8818 (admin)

15. **Contact-a-Family,** 170 Tottenham Court Road, London W1P OHA. 0171-383 3555

16. **Counsel and Care for the Elderly,** Twyman House, 16 Bonny Street, London NW1 9PG. 0171-485 1566

17. **Disability Alliance,** 1st Floor East, Universal House, 88-94 Wentworth Street, London E1 7SA.   0171-247 8776

18. **Disability Network,** 8 Wolverhampton House, 123 Church Street, St Helens, Merseyside WA9 1JS.   01744-451215

19. **Disabled Living Foundation,** 380-4 Harrow Road, London W9 2HU.   0171-289 6111

20. **Eyeline,** c/o Janet Wallace, 22 Whitaker Lane, Prestwich, Manchester M25 5FX. 0161-872 1234

21. **Guide Dogs for the Blind Association/Guide Dogs Adventure Group,** Hillfields, Burghfield, Reading, Berks RG7 3YG. 01734-835555

22. **Help the Aged,** St James's Walk, London EC1R 0BE. 0171-253 0253

23. **Holiday Care Service,** 2 Old Bank Chambers, Station Road, Horley, Surrey RH6 9HW.   01293-774535

24. **Horticultural Therapy,** 1 Goulds Ground, Vallis Way, Frome, Somerset BA11 3DW. 01373-467072

25. **Living Paintings Trust,** Silchester House, Silchester, Berkshire RG7 2LT. 01734-700776

26. **LOOK (National Federation of Families with Visually Impaired Children),** c/o Queen Alexandra College, 49 Court Oak Road, Harborne, Birmingham B17 9TG. 0121-428 5038

27. **National Association of Toy and Leisure Libraries/Play Matters,** 68 Church Way, London NW1 1LT.   0171-387 9592

28. **National Childbirth Trust and ParentAbility,** Alexandra House, Oldham Terrace, London W3 6NH.   0181-992 8637

29. **National Debtline,** Birmingham Settlement, 318 Summer Lane, Birmingham B19 3AL. 0121-359 8501

30. **National Federation of the Blind,** Unity House, Smyth Street, Westgate, Wakefield , West Yorks WF1 1ER.   01924-29 1313

31. **National Library for the Blind,** Cromwell Road, Bredbury, Stockport SK6 2SG. 0161-494 0217

32. **National Trust,** 36 Queen Anne's Gate, London SW1H 9AS.   0171-222 9251

33. **Organisation of Blind Afric-Caribbeans,** 24 Maywood House, Benhill Road, London SE5 7NA.   0171-703 3688

34. **Partially Sighted Society,** Queens Road, Doncaster DN1 2NX (admin, membership, publications).   01302-323132
London office (general enquiries, low vision adviser).   0171-372 1551

35. **RADAR,** 12 City Forum, 250 City Road, London EC1V 8AF.   0171-250 3222

36. **Royal National Institute for the Blind,** 224 Great Portland Street, London W1N 6AA. 0171-388 1266

Please contact the above address for the following services:

RNIB Benefit Rights and Information Team
RNIB Community Education Office
RNIB Development Officer for Ethnic
      Minorities
RNIB Education Information Service
RNIB Employment Network

RNIB Grants and Information Officer
RNIB Hotels and Holiday Service
RNIB Leisure Service
RNIB/GDBA Mobility Unit
RNIB Ophthalmic Advisory Service
RNIB Reference Library
RNIB Resource Centre, London
RNIB Voluntary Agencies Link Unit

37. **RNIB Advocacy Service for Parents,** c/o RNIB New College Worcester, Whittington Road, Worcester WR5 2JX. 01905-357635 (24 hour answerphone service 01678-41429)

38. **RNIB Customer Services,** PO Box 173, Peterborough PE2 6WS.   0345-023153 (for the price of a local call)

Please contact the above address for the following services:

RNIB Customer Services (sales of publications in large print, braille, Moon and on tape; games and equipment; transcription service and advice)
RNIB Braille Library
RNIB Cassette Library

39. RNIB Employment Network

London and South, RNIB, 224 Great Portland Street, London W1N 6AA. 0171-388 1266

Central England and Wales, RNIB, 7 The Square, 111 Broad Street, Birmingham B15 1AF.   0121-631 3372

North West England, RNIB, Crown House, 2nd Floor, 10-12 James Street, Liverpool L2 7PQ.   0151-255 0562

Scotland, RNIB, 10 Magdala Crescent, Edinburgh EH12 5BE.   0131-313 1877

North East England, RNIB, 5 Skinnergate, Darlington, Durham DL3 7AB. 01325-364913

South West, RNIB, c/o BRSB, Stillhouse Lane, Bedminster, Bristol BS3 4EB. 01179-537750

40. **RNIB Housing Service,** Garrow House, 190 Kensal Road, North Kensington, London W10 5BT. 0181-969 2380

41. **RNIB Northern Ireland Service Bureau,** 40 Linenhall Street, Belfast BT2 8BG. 01232-329373

42. **RNIB Rehabilitation Centres**

   RNIB Alwyn House, 3 Wemysshall Road, Ceres, Cupar, Fife KY15 5LX. 0133482-8894/5/6

   RNIB Manor House, Middle Lincombe Road, Torquay, Devon TQ1 2NG. 01803-214523

43. **RNIB Resource Centre Stirling,** 9 Viewfield Place, Stirling FK8 1NL.   01786-451752

44. **RNIB Student Support Service,** PO Box 49, Loughborough, Leicestershire LE11 3DG. 01509-211995

45. **RNIB Talking Book Service,** Mount Pleasant, Wembley, Middlesex HA0 1RR. 0345-626843

46. **Scottish Braille Press,** Craigmillar Park, Edinburgh EH16 5NB.   0131-662 4445

47. **Sense (National Association for Deaf/Blind and Rubella Handicapped),** 11-13 Clifton Terrace, London N4 3SR.   0171-272 7774

48. **Talking Newspaper Association of the UK (TNAUK),** National Recording Centre, Heathfield, East Sussex TN21 8DB. 01435-866102

49. **Telephones for the Blind Fund,** 7 Huntersfield Close, Reigate, Surrey RH2 0PX.   01737-248032

50. **Torch Trust for the Blind,** Torch House, Hallaton, Market Harborough, Leicestershire LE16 8UJ.   01858-89301

51. **Tripscope,** The Courtyard, Evelyn Road, London W4 5JL.   0181-994 9294

52. **Vision Aid,** c/o Lesley Green, 22a Chorley New Road, Bolton BL1 4AP.   01204-31882

53. **WRVS,** 234-244 Stockwell Road, London SW9 9SP.   0171-416 0146

A short guide to benefits

The list on the following pages shows some of the benefits and concessions you may be entitled to as a blind or partially sighted person. In some cases you need to be registered to claim them (see chapter 2 on registration for more detail on this). Some benefits are also means-tested.

Not all the benefits mentioned here are available to blind and partially sighted people alike. We have abbreviated 'blind' and 'partially sighted' to 'b' and 'ps' to indicate who may be able to claim what.

For fuller information on benefits, please see chapter 5.

		Benefit/concession Statutory sources	Remarks
B		Blind person's personal income tax allowance	Available to blind people. Can be transferred to your partner on request.
B	**PS**	Disability Living Allowance (DLA)/ Attendance Allowance (AA)	For help with personal care and mobility. DLA must be claimed before your 66th birthday. Those over 66 can claim AA. Contact your local social security office, or phone the Benefits Enquiry Line 0800-882200.
B	**PS**	Additional Income Support	Contact your local Benefits Agency office or phone 0800-882200 and ask about the additional *premiums* you could get.
B	**PS**	Additional Housing Benefit or Council Tax Benefit or both	Contact your local council Housing Benefit or Council Tax Benefit sections and ask about additional *premiums*.
B	**PS**	Help towards the cost of residential or nursing home fees	Financial help towards residential/nursing home costs may be available. Contact your local council social services department or phone 0800-882200.

		Benefit/concession Statutory sources	Remarks
3	PS	Severe Disablement Allowance	This is for people of working age who are incapable of work. Housewives (or male equivalent) are encouraged to claim. Contact your local Benefits Agency office or phone 0800-882200.
3	PS	Disability Working Allowance	For disabled people on low incomes working over 16 hours per week. Contact your local Benefits Agency office or phone 0800-882200.
3	PS	Community care services and assistance from your local council	You are entitled to ask your council to assess your need for services such as home care, mobility training, counselling, equipment or home adaptations. Contact your local council social services department.
3	PS	Exemption from 'non-dependants' deduction from Income Support, Housing Benefit and Council Tax Benefit	Deductions for non-dependants living in your home are not made. Ask for a written breakdown of benefit to check that you are not paying for a non-dependant, or how you could be exempt.

		Benefit/concession Statutory sources	Remarks
B	PS	Free NHS sight test	Tell the optometrist about your registration before th sight test.
B	PS	Low vision aids (such as magnifiers)	Discuss with your eye specialist or contact the Partially Sighted Society on 0171-372 1551.
B		Reduction in television licence fee	Currently £1.25 less than standard rate.
B		Car parking concessions under the Orange Badge Scheme	The car does not need to b yours. Contact your local social services department for more information.
B	PS	Special equipment and practical help for work under the 'Access to Work' scheme	Can be provided by the Department of Employmen Details from Jobcentres anc RNIB Employment Networ
B	PS	Practical and financial help with journeys to work	May be available to visually impaired workers unable to use public transport. Contact your local Jobcentre and ask about 'Fares to work' scheme.

		Benefit/concession Statutory sources	Remarks
3	**PS**	Free postage on items marked 'articles for the blind'	Applies to braille items or recordings like Talking Books, but not personal tapes and letters. Contact RNIB Customer Services (address 38 on page 127) for details.
3	**PS**	Special arrangements for voting at elections	Contact your local council and ask about postal or proxy voting well before the election.
3	**PS**	Free NHS prescriptions	For people on low incomes and for those unable to go out without help. Ask RNIB Benefit Rights and Information Team for details (address 36 on page 126).

		Benefit/concession Public sector sources	Remarks
B	**PS**	Railcard and other travel concessions on British Rail	Contact your nearest British Rail station or RNIB/GDBA Mobility Unit on 0171-388 1266.
B	**PS**	Local travel schemes	Contact your local council for details of travel concessions in your area.
B	**PS**	Exemption from British Telecom and Mercury Directory Enquiry charges	Telephone 0800-919195 (B or 0800-424194 (Mercury) for details.
B		Free permanent loan of radio and TV sound receivers	Contact your local council social services department and ask about the British Wireless for the Blind Fun
B		Help with telephone rental and installation charges	Contact your local council social services department or Telephones for the Blin Fund, 7 Huntersfield Clos Reigate, Surrey RH2 0PX. Telephone 01737-248032.

Index

Benefits Agency, 1, 30, 64
Benefits Agency Benefits Enquiry Line, 63
Big Print, 33, 78
bills, large print and braille, 29-30, 77
Blind Business Association, 101
Blind Person's Tax Allowance, 65, 68, 70, 132
blindness, 13
braille, 29-31, 80-82, 86
brain, 8-9, 13
British Blind Sport, 83-84, 113
British Gas, 30, 39
British Rail, 72, 136
British Red Cross, 34
British Wireless for the Blind Fund, 136
building societies, 29
bus permit schemes, 72

Calibre, 79
Care and Repair, 58
careers **see** jobs
carers, 46-47, 70-71
cataract, 9, 17
cheque templates, 29, 42
children, 104-115
Citizens Advice Bureaux, 1, 64, 75
cleaning **see** housework
closed-circuit television, 18
coach journeys **see** travel
coin holders, 41

grants, for students, 111-112
guide dogs, 35-36
Guide Dogs Adventure Group, 88
Guide Dogs for the Blind Association, 36

Health and Social Services Boards, 2, 26
higher education, 110-112
hobbies, 84-86
Holiday Care Service, 90
holidays, 88-90
    for children, 113-114
holistic medicine, 15
home help, 45
home improvements, 56-58
home-working schemes, 101
homeless, 58-59
homoeopathy, 15
Horticultural Therapy, 87
hospital, 17-18
hotels, 88, 89
housework, 36-39
housing associations, 52
housing, 46, 51-59
Housing Benefit, 67, 69, 73-74, 132

Incapacity Benefit, 68
income tax allowance **see** Blind Person's Tax
    Allowance
Income Support, 67, 69, 132
information, finding, 29, 32-33

Organisation of Blind Afric-Caribbeans, 44
orthoptist, 7, 104
owner-occupiers, 53-54, 57

PACTs **see** Placing, Assessment and Counselling
    Teams
paperwork, 29, 31
ParentAbility, 114
parents, 104-107 **see also** visually impaired
    parents
    support groups, 106
Partially Sighted Society, 19
pension book templates, 42
pensions **see** benefits
Placing, Assessment and Counselling Teams
    (PACTs), 94, 96, 98
playing cards, 84
post **see** paperwork
postage **see** 'articles for the blind' scheme
prescriptions, 135
public libraries, 78, 79

radio, 32
    loan of, 136
Radio Times, in braille, 82
railways, **see** British Rail, travel
readers, 31, 96
reading, 77-83
Record of special educational needs, 109-110
registration, 26-28, 47
rehabilitation, for work, 98, 100